DOWN OUR WAY

Developmental Reading Series

A BASIC READING PROGRAM

DOWN OUR WAY

by

GUY L. BOND

GRACE A. DORSEY   MARIE C. CUDDY

KATHLEEN WISE

PRINTED IN THE UNITED STATES OF AMERICA
PRINTED IN THE UNITED STATES OF AMERICA

Copyright 1954, 1949 by

LYONS AND CARNAHAN

CHICAGO   DALLAS,   ATLANTA   WILKES-BARRE
PASADENA   SAN FRANCISCO

401N58

STORIES

Summer Time

Money for the Circus

The circus was coming soon.
Billy and Jack March wanted
to see it.

"We must have some money
for the circus," said Billy.

"How can we get the money?"
asked Jack.

"I do not know," answered Billy.
"I think we can find some work
that we can do."

"Look, this is July," said Jack.
"Here is the day that the circus
is coming."

Jack put a big X on the four.

"Yes," said Billy. "The circus
will come on the Fourth of July
We have two days to work and
get some money."

"That is not so very long, is it,"
said Jack. "We will ask Mother
what to do."

"There are many things that you can do," said Mother. "There are strawberries ready to be picked."

Mother got a box for each boy.

"Put the strawberries you pick into the little boxes," she said.

"We can not put many strawberries in those little boxes," said Jack. "We can not get money for the circus with them."

"Here is a basket," said Mother.
"Every time your little box is full,
take it to the basket. You can put
those strawberries into the basket."

Billy said, "We will not know
how much money each of us gets."

"Put X on the box each time you
get it full," said Mother. "Then you
will know how many boxes full
of strawberries you picked."

"How much money will you give
us for each box of strawberries?"
asked Jack. "Will you give us
five cents?"

"Yes, I will give you five cents
for each full box," answered Mother.

"Good!" said Billy. "Come on,
Jack. We have work to do."

Jack picked up the basket and
one of the little boxes.

"I am going to work very fast,"
said Jack. "Every X that we put
on a box will be five cents for us.
It will not take long to get our
money for the Fourth of July."

Did Judy Help?

Billy and Jack went to the garden. They began to work.

Soon they had picked some boxes of strawberries. The big basket was almost full.

Judy went out to the garden to see what the boys were doing. She saw the red strawberries in the basket. Um-um, um-um! Those strawberries looked good.

Judy liked strawberries very much. She began to eat some of them.

Jack came to put some strawberries into the basket.

"Where did our strawberries go?" said Jack. "Our big basket was almost full."

Then he saw Judy. Something red was all over her face.

"Oh, just look at Judy's red face," said her brother Jack. "Now I know where those strawberries went."

"Judy picked strawberries, too," said Billy. "She picked them out of our basket."

"Our sister looks almost as funny
as a circus clown," said Jack.

"Here comes Daddy. Show him
your funny face," said Billy.

Judy ran to show Daddy her face.

"I helped my brothers," she said.
"I picked the most strawberries."

Daddy laughed when he saw Judy.

"I think I know where you put
the strawberries," he said.

Daddy went to work in his garden.
He pulled out most of the weeds.

Judy was in the garden with Daddy.
She wanted to help pull weeds.

She showed Daddy all the weeds
she had pulled.

"Please may I have five cents?"
asked Judy. "I helped pull weeds out
of our garden."

Daddy laughed and laughed when
he saw what Judy had pulled.

"Those are not weeds," said Daddy.
"You are too little to do much work
in our garden. But I will give you
five cents."

The Fourth of July

When the Fourth of July came,
the children got up early.

"Today is the Fourth of July,"
said Billy. "It is the birthday
of our country."

"We will put on our hats and
march around the yard," said Jack.
"Our dog Tricks can march with us."

Jack got some hats. The hats
were red, white, and blue.

He gave one to his brother and
one to his sister.

The children went into the yard.
Around and around they marched.

Mr. March heard the parade and
looked out of the window.

"I will get out the large flag,"
he said. "The flag of our country
must be in the parade today."

Daddy got a large flag. He marched with the children. Then he put the large flag on the house.

"Now please sing about our flag," said Mother.

The children began to sing, "Hurrah for the red, white, and blue."

Hurrah for the Circus!

Daddy and the children helped
Mother with her work. When the
work was done, they all got ready
to go to the circus.

Soon they got into their car and
away they went to the circus. They
wanted to get there early to see
the circus animals. They wanted
to see the parade, too.

"Hurrah for the Fourth of July!
Hurrah for the circus!" shouted Jack.
"Hurrah! Hurrah!"

Near the circus the children saw
a man who had balloons and flags.

"Please may I have one of those
large balloons?" asked Judy.

Jack gave the man five cents.
He got a balloon for his sister.

"Now we will see the animals,"
said Daddy.

Billy shouted, "Hurrah! I want
to see the monkeys most of all.

"I want to see the elephants, too."

There were elephants in the tent.
Many of them were large. One was
a little elephant. The circus man
said its name was Choto.

Soon Choto saw the red balloon
in Judy's hands. The elephant put
out his trunk. He got the balloon
and waved it.

"Oh, look what Choto has done,"
said Judy. "He has my balloon.
Please make him give it back."

"Choto thinks it is his balloon," said the man. "He has a balloon when he is in the circus parade.

"Here are some peanuts. Choto likes them very much. When he sees the peanuts, Choto will put down the balloon right away."

Choto waved the balloon. Then he smelled the peanuts. He put down the balloon.

"Throw some peanuts to him now," said the man.

Choto ate all the peanuts.

A man came by with a large box.
He was going to feed the monkeys.

"You may come with me, Billy,"
said the man. "I am going to feed
the monkeys early today. You may
help me feed them."

The monkeys ate what Billy gave
them.

Billy had fun with the monkeys.
One little monkey tried to get
Billy's hat.

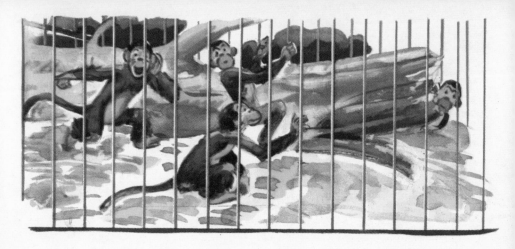

"Look out, Billy!" called the man.
"Do not let the monkey get your hat.
He will not give it back. He has
done that trick before."

"Oh!" said Billy. "He almost got
my hat that time.

"I must go now. It was so much
fun to feed the monkeys. They ate
right from my hand. I want to
thank you for the good time."

The man shook hands with Billy.

"Thank you for helping me feed
the monkeys," said the man.

The Big Show

Many people were in the big tent.
It was almost time for the circus
to begin.

Before the circus began, there was
a big parade. A band played for the
parade. Some big red circus wagons
came into the tent. There were
animals in the wagons.

Then some white horses came in.
There was a girl on each horse.
Around and around went the horses.

A donkey walked into the tent.
A clown was on the donkey. The
clown had a funny face.

The donkey turned around and saw
the funny face. He stopped. He would
not go. The clown tried to make him
go. The clown waved a large stick,
but the donkey would not go.

Another clown ran to the donkey.
The clown opened his large mouth
and began to sing. Away went
the donkey.

"He runs when I begin to sing,"
said the clown.

The people laughed at what
the clown had done.

Then two white horses came in.
A circus man had one of his feet
on each of the horses.

"Look!" said Jack. "That man
can ride two horses."

Just then another clown went by.
He had a little red wagon.

"Oh, look!" shouted Jack. "That
is the best clown in the circus."

The clown heard what Jack said.

"Do you want a ride in my wagon?"
called Boo, the clown. "You will
have the best ride in the circus."

When Jack got into the wagon,
the clown began to walk.

Just then there was a noise.
Bang, bang, bang went something
on the back of the wagon. Bang,
bang, bang, bang it went four
more times.

"Please look out now, Jack,"
called the clown. "We will begin
to go fast right now."

The clown began to run very fast.
He ran around the tent three times.

The people clapped and clapped
their hands when Jack went by.
Jack waved to the people.

As soon as the ride was done,
Jack shook hands with Boo.

"Thank you for the ride," he said.
"That was fun. When I am a man,
I will be a clown."

The Ride to Fox Lake

One morning Mr. March said, "I do not have to work this week. We will go to Fox Lake."

All three of the children clapped their hands.

"Oh, good, good!" shouted Jack. "Will we take the tent with us?"

"Yes, we will take the tent," said Daddy. "You may help me put it on the car right now."

"We can catch fish at Fox Lake," said Billy. "Will we have a boat?"

"Yes," answered Daddy. "This summer you may row the boat."

"Please may I row the boat, too?" asked Judy.

"No, not this summer," answered Mother. "You are too little to row. You and I will ride in the boat. Your brothers will row it."

Judy put her toys into the car. The boys helped Mother and Daddy get ready to go to the lake. When their work was done, away they went in the car.

After a time Jack saw a big sign. It said: *Eat Here.*

"See that sign, Daddy," said Jack. "It is the best sign on the road. Please may we stop there? It is almost time for lunch."

"Yes," said Daddy. "We will eat lunch early today."

Daddy stopped the car near some little houses. Near the houses there was a big sign.

"Who lives in those houses?"
asked Judy.

"Those houses are for tourists,"
answered Billy. "That big sign
said Tourist Camp."

"We are tourists, now," said Jack.
"Is there a tourist camp at Fox Lake?"

"Yes, there is," answered Daddy.
"There are no houses at that camp.
It is the best tourist camp for people
who have tents."

After lunch they got into the car
and went on down the road.

Billy and Jack saw a large trailer.
They could see two boys in the car.

"Those people may be going to stop
at the Fox Lake Tourist Camp, too,"
said Jack. "That big boy could show
me how to row a boat. The boys can
swim with us, too."

Soon the car came to another sign.
It said: *Fox Lake Tourist Camp*
for Tents and Trailers
Turn Right.

"That trailer is going to turn
at the tourist camp," said Billy.
"It is turning in there now."

"Good," said Jack. "We will get
those boys to swim with us."

"It will not take very much time
to put up our tent," said Daddy.
"We will begin now. When we
are done we will go for a swim."

"Hurrah!" shouted Jack. "Hurrah
for Fox Lake! It is the best lake
in the country."

Judy clapped her hands.

"Hurrah, hurrah!" she shouted.

Fun at Fox Lake

All week the three children had fun at Fox Lake. Every day they all went for a swim. The boys from the trailer went with them.

One day Jim showed Judy something that looked like a large balloon.

"This is a toy duck," said Jim. "It will take you for a ride."

Jim put Judy on the large duck. Away she went for a ride.

All week Tom and Jim tried to show Billy how to row a boat.

At first Billy could not row well. He splashed water all over the boat.

Billy tried again and again to row the boat. By the time a week was over, he could row very well.

"Good for you, Billy," said Jim. "You have done well. Now you row almost as well as your daddy."

Daddy and Jack went fishing. They
did not catch any fish at first.

"They will begin to bite soon,"
said Daddy.

Daddy pulled in a fish. Then he
had another bite. Soon Daddy had
four fish.

Daddy said, "Now we have fish
to feed the hungry people at camp.
They can eat fish all week."

"Hurrah!" shouted Jack. "I have
my first bite. I think that it is
a very big fish."

Jack pulled and pulled.

"Do you want any help, Jack?"
called Daddy.

"No, I think I can pull it in,"
answered Jack.

Up came a big weed. When Jack
saw it, he laughed.

"I could not feed that weed to any
people at our camp," he said.

"Now you have a good fish story
for them," said Daddy. "I think you
will get a bite soon."

Before long, Jack and Daddy
had many fish.

When Daddy and Jack got back
to the camp, Judy saw all their fish.

"I will catch some fish, too,"
she said.

First, Judy went into the water.
She could see many little fish there.
She wanted them. She clapped her
hands under the water.

Judy tried and tried, but she could
not catch any fish.

"They look like toy fish, but
they swim very fast," called Judy.
"I can not catch them."

"Well, let them go," said Daddy.
"You may eat some of our fish."

Story Time at Camp

It was story time at the tourist
camp. Jim was ready to begin a
story. This is Jim's story:

Three Monkeys in a Trailer

Some people by the name of Best
had a new trailer. Early one morning
they were going to the country
for a picnic.

It was the Fourth of July, so
Mr. Best put flags on the trailer.
The boys made a large sign that
said: *Hurrah for the Fourth.*

Away they all went in their new trailer. After a time Mr. Best stopped the trailer near a lake.

"Please may we all go for a swim now?" asked the boys.

Soon every one went to the lake.

Three monkeys were in a tree near the trailer. They came down and looked in the open window. Right into the trailer they went.

One of the monkeys saw three cents. He picked them up in his queer hands. He turned the money over and over. He tried to bite it. What a funny face the monkey made!

Another monkey saw a box that was
full of strawberries. The monkey
began to take them out of the box.
He ate some of them.

He put most of the strawberries
in a long row. He walked up and down
the row and looked at the strawberries.

Every time the monkey turned
around, his tail hit some of the
strawberries. Soon there were not
any of the strawberries in the row.
They were all over the trailer.

One little monkey saw a balloon.
He picked it up and waved it. Just
as soon as the other monkeys saw
the balloon, they wanted it.

Out of the window went the monkey
with the balloon. The other monkeys
were just behind him.

Up, up they went on the trailer.

One of the monkeys saw a flag.
He wanted it very much. He got it.

The two monkeys marched up and
down. One of them waved a flag
and one waved a balloon.

At first the other monkey did not
know what to do. He wanted to be
in the parade. He did not have
any flag. He did not have any balloon.
He had no toy at all.

Soon he jumped down and pulled up
a big weed. It was almost as pretty
as the balloon. Then he ran right
back to march in the parade.

When Mr. Best came from the lake, he saw the monkeys.

"Well, well!" shouted Mr. Best. "Look at the monkeys on our trailer. How did they get here?"

Just then a man came to the trailer. His name was Jack.

"Those three monkeys are from my brother's tourist camp," the man said. "They ran away. They did not come home all week. They have done that before."

"How will you catch the monkeys?"
asked Tom Best.

"I will call to them and show them
something to eat," answered the man.
"When I feed them, they will go home
with me."

Just then, one monkey clapped his
hands on the balloon. Then bang
went the balloon.

Down from the trailer came those
three monkeys. They ran to the man.

"They will be glad to go home now,"
said the man.

Away he went with the three funny
little monkeys.

Friends Around Town

The Vegetable Man

An old white horse pulled a wagon down the streets of the town.

The man in the wagon had come to town with vegetables.

The man called out so people would know he had vegetables to sell.

"Vegetables, vegetables!" he called. "Get vegetables here!"

Mrs. Brown heard the man call out about the vegetables.

"I must buy some vegetables," she said. "I do not have a garden."

Mrs. Brown called to the man, and he stopped his horse.

"I want to buy some vegetables," said Mrs. Brown. "I have a box ready to put them in."

Soon the box was full of vegetables. Just then Jack March came down the street. He saw Mrs. Brown and her big box.

"Do you want me to help you?" called Jack.

"Yes, I do," answered Mrs. Brown. "I shall be very glad to have help."

Jack helped Mrs. Brown take the box of vegetables into her house.

"I have a big garden," said Jack. "I think I will sell some vegetables. I want to get money for a football."

"You can sell to the neighbors," said Mrs. Brown. "I shall be glad to buy some."

"Thank you," said Jack. "I think I will be a vegetable man."

Money for a Football

Jack March got some vegetables out of his own garden. He put the vegetables into his wagon. Then he looked for his sister Judy.

"I thought you would like to help sell vegetables," said Jack. "I will pull the wagon. You may ride."

"Good," said Judy. "I will call out just like the vegetable man."

Jack put a large hat on his sister.

"Now you look like a vegetable man," he said.

Jack pulled the little wagon down the street.

"Vegetables!" Judy called out. "Vegetables to sell! Buy fresh vegetables for your dinner!"

"There is a new vegetable man in town," said Mrs. Brown. "What do you have to sell?"

"I have many fresh vegetables from my own garden," said Jack. "I just picked them this morning. Would you like to buy any of my vegetables for your dinner?"

Mrs. Stone came out of her house.

She asked if Jack got the vegetables
from his own garden.

"Yes," answered Jack. "I thought
I would sell them so I can get money
to buy a football."

"I can always use fresh vegetables,"
said Mrs. Stone. "I shall be glad
to buy all you want to sell me."

Jack thanked Mrs. Stone when she
gave him the money. Then he went
down the street.

What Shall I Buy?

Jack and Judy looked at the money they got for the vegetables.

"We can buy ice cream," said Judy. "We will buy all the ice cream that we can eat."

"This is my own money," said Jack. I like ice cream myself, but I thought I would keep this money. I am going to use most of it to buy a football."

"I helped you sell the vegetables," said Judy. "I made people come out to buy the vegetables."

Jack looked at Judy and laughed.

"Yes, you helped me very much," said Jack. "I thought I would keep the money for a football, but we might buy ice cream for our dinner with some of the money."

Jack and Judy went to a store and got some ice cream. Um-um, how good it was.

"I can sell more vegetables some day," said Jack. "I will have more money to use for my football."

Mother thanked Jack and Judy
for the ice cream.

"I am glad you are going to keep
some of your money," said Mother.
"Before long you will have enough
to buy your football."

"Every time I sell vegetables I will
keep some of the money for myself,"
said Jack. "It will be fun to buy
my own football."

"It has been fun to buy ice cream,
too," said Judy.

Market Day

Mrs. March was going down town
to the big market. She wanted to buy
many things.

"Judy and I are ready to go,"
called Mrs. March. "Are you boys
ready to go to town?"

"We have been ready a long time,"
answered Billy. "I have the large
market basket. We can put fresh fruit
and other things you buy into it."

Soon Mrs. March and the children
were at the market.

"I thought we might buy peaches
for dinner," said Mother. "Look
for the sign so we will know where
to buy them."

Jack showed Mother a large sign
that said: *Buy Fresh Fruit Here.*

Mrs. March picked out the peaches
she liked best. She gave the peaches
to a man in the market.

"I think that will be enough peaches
for us," she said. "Will you see how
much they weigh?"

After the peaches had been weighed,
the man put them into a yellow
basket. He put something red over
the peaches.

"Can you use any other fresh fruit
today?" asked the man. "Do you want
any fresh vegetables?"

"No," answered Mrs. March. "I have
enough fruit now. We have vegetables
in our own garden. But I would like
some honey."

Mrs. March gave money to the man.

"Thank you very much," he said.
"Call again."

The New Kitty

Judy saw a little white kitty.
"I wish I could have a kitty.
I have been wanting a little kitty
just for myself," she said.

Billy and Jack looked to see how
much money they had. They wanted
to buy the kitty for their sister.

Jack asked the man how much
money he wanted for the kitty.
Billy and Jack gave their money
to the man.

The man said, "You might carry
the kitty in this fruit basket."

"I wish you would weigh the kitty,"
said Judy. "I want to know how much
it weighs."

The man weighed the kitty. He put
it into a basket. He put something
over the yellow basket. He gave the
basket to Judy.

"Now I can carry it," said Judy.
"It looks like a basket of peaches."

Judy clapped her hands.

"Oh, now I know what to name
this dear little kitty," she said.
"I will call her Peachy."

Just then a large dog walked
into the market. He saw a little
kitty in a box and he ran to it.

"Bow wow," said the dog.

The mother cat had been behind
a box. She heard the dog.

Out came the cat. She put out
her paw. Up went her back.

"F-ff-t, f-ff-t!" said the cat.
"F-ff-t, f-ff-t, f-ff-t!"

Away went the dog just as fast
as he could go.

Lunch at the Market

"Now we shall buy a chicken and some fresh eggs," said Mother.

A man weighed the chicken and put it into Billy's large basket.

"I guess you can carry the chicken," said the man. "I shall give the eggs to your mother."

"I feel hungry," said Jack. "I wish I could have some milk."

"I think all of us would like some milk," said Mother. "Then we shall go home. Soon it will be time for me to get dinner."

Mother and the children stopped
to get some milk.

"I wish Peachy could have some
milk," said Judy. "She is hungry."

"Peachy cannot have milk now,
dear," said Mother. "When we get
home, you may give her some milk."

Jack began to laugh.

"What do you think Tricks will do
when he sees Peachy?" he asked.

"We might have to get the old cat
that was at the market," answered
his brother. "She would tell Tricks
to keep away from Peachy."

Good Friends

Judy walked into the yard. She had her yellow basket. The new kitty was in the basket.

Tricks ran to Judy. He sniffed and sniffed the basket.

Peachy got out of her little basket. When Tricks saw her, he began to bark.

"F-ff-t, f-ff-t!" said Peachy.

"Don't bark at dear little Peachy," said Judy. "She might run away."

Mother got a dish. She put milk
in it for Peachy. She got a big dish
of food for Tricks.

Mother said, "We will feed the pets.
We shall put the dishes of food near
each other.

Tricks knows this dish is for him.
The little kitty will see her food
in the other dish."

Tricks began to eat from his dish.
He stopped and looked at Peachy, but
he did not bark. He just ate his food.

Peachy looked at Tricks a long time.
Then she walked over to her dish
of milk.

"Oh good," said Judy. "I knew
Tricks and Peachy would be friends.
Now they can play with each other."

Just then, Peachy saw Tricks' tail
going from side to side. She put
out her paw.

"Oh dear, don't do that," said Judy.
"Tricks might bite you."

Billy said, "Tricks will not bite her.
He and Peachy are good friends now."

When night came, Judy wished she
had a bed for Peachy.

"Don't you want to use this box?"
asked Mother. "It is just big enough
for a bed for Peachy. It is almost
time for you to go to bed, too."

Judy made a bed for the kitty.
She put Peachy into it.

"Good night, dear little Peachy,"
said Judy. "Now I am going to bed
myself. I shall see you early
in the morning."

That night Tricks heard Peachy get
out of bed. He ran to Mr. March and
began to bark. He pulled and pulled
to make Mr. March go with him.

Mr. March saw Peachy. She had
been out of her bed long enough
to be cold.

"Mew, mew, mew," she said.

Mr. March put Peachy back into bed.

"You have been a good dog, Tricks,"
he said. "You knew how to get help
for your new friend."

The Dairy

Tim Camp worked for the Park
Dairy. He had to take milk
to people all over town.

Blackie was the horse that pulled
the dairy wagon. Tim liked the horse.
He gave candy to Blackie every
morning.

"Old Blackie likes sweet food,"
said Tim. "I have something sweet
for him every morning. I give it
to him just before we go to town.
Blackie and I are very good friends."

One day Billy got up early and
went to the dairy with Tim.

Tim was going to let Billy ride
around town in the big yellow
dairy wagon.

Many farm trucks were at the dairy.
There were large cans of fresh milk
on each truck.

A man weighed the cans of milk.
Then he put the milk in the dairy.

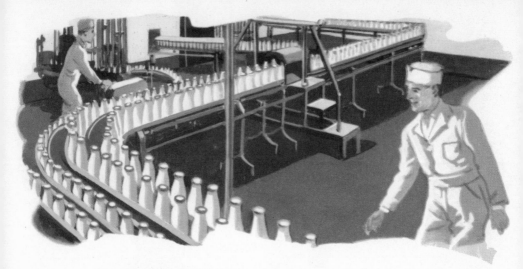

Tim said, "We shall not have time to see all of the dairy this morning. We do many things with the milk before it is ready to go into bottles.

"You might like to see how the milk is put into bottles. We have time to see that."

At one side of the dairy Billy saw a large machine. Many bottles were going around on it. Each bottle stopped. When the bottle was full of milk, the machine made it go on.

"The wagon is ready," called Tim. "Now Blackie will take us around town. You can help me carry the bottles of milk to people's homes."

Down the street went the dairy wagon. Blackie stopped at a house.

"What made Blackie stop?" asked Billy. "I did not hear you tell him to stop."

"I did not have to tell Blackie," answered Tim. "He knew just where to stop.

When we carry the milk into the houses, Blackie will go on. He will go to the next house on this side of the street. He will wait there."

"He is like the machine that puts milk into the bottles," said Billy. "He knows just when to wait and just when to go."

"He is a good dairy horse," said Tim.

76

The Best Horse in Town

There was a fire down the street.

Blackie could not see the fire, but
he could hear the fire truck.

"Now see what our horse will do,"
said Tim. "He knows enough to stop
when he hears the fire truck coming."

Blackie pulled over to the side
of the street and stopped.

Down the street came the fire truck.
Blackie waited for the fire truck
to go by. Then he went on.

At the next street there was a red
light.

"Will Blackie stop for the light?"
asked Billy.

"The horse cannot see the light,
but he will stop," answered Tim.
"He always stops at a new street.
Blackie waits for me to tell him
when to go to the other side."

"I think you have the best horse
in town," said Billy.

Soon Tim said there were no more bottles of milk to carry.

"I shall take you to the dairy barn," said Tim. "You will see the big barn where Blackie lives. You will see what he gets for food.

"There are many horses in the barn. I don't know much about them myself. My friend Jerry will tell you what you want to hear about them."

Back at the Dairy

Jerry showed Billy the big barn.
The horses were eating their food.

Then Jerry wanted to show Billy
something new.

"We don't carry all the milk
in wagons," said Jerry. "We use
many trucks. Here is a new truck
that just came in this morning."

"It is a good truck," said Billy.
"You have many good horses, too,
but I like Blackie better than
the others."

Just then Tim called to Billy.

"Come with me, Billy," he said.
"I shall show you a big machine
we use. You will like this machine
better than any other."

Billy saw the large machines
that made ice cream.

"Um-um, um-um," said Billy.
"That ice cream looks good."

A man got dishes of ice cream
for Billy and Tim.

"I knew you would like ice cream,"
said the man. "If that is not enough,
you may have more."

That night Jack and Judy wanted
to hear all Billy had to tell them.

"I wish that I could have been
with Mr. Camp today," said Jack.

"He knew you would like to go
with him," said Billy. "He said
to tell you that he might take you
next week. You will see the barns
and the dairy horses. You will see
the large trucks, too."

"I just want to see enough
of that ice cream," said Jack.

The Firemen Help Peachy

Peachy had been playing in the yard
for a long time. A large dog was
in the next yard. When the dog
saw Peachy, he barked and barked
at her.

Away went Peachy as fast as she
could go. She ran up a big tree.
Up, up, up she went.

When the dog went away, Peachy
wanted to come down. She did not
know how to get to the ground.

"Mew, mew," she called.

Tricks heard little Peachy calling.
He did not know what to do at first.
Then he saw Mother.

Tricks ran to Mother and barked.
Then he pulled Mother to the tree.

When Mother was near the tree,
she could hear the kitty mewing.
Mother called Jack and Judy.

"Peachy has been up in the tree
a long time," she said. "Get a dish
of milk. That might make her come
down."

Peachy wanted the food, but she
did not know how to come down.

"Oh dear!" said Mother. "I had better call the firemen. They can get the kitty."

Soon the firemen came. They got Peachy.

"Here, Judy, you take the kitty," said one of the firemen.

"Thank you," said Judy. "I am so glad you got Peachy for me."

"Thank Tricks more than you thank us," said one of the firemen. "Tricks showed you where Peachy went."

"Tricks is Peachy's best friend," said Judy.

The Fire at the Market

"Fire! The big market is on fire!"
shouted a man. "Call the firemen!"

The people at the market began
to carry out their things. Out came
people with fresh vegetables and
fruits and other foods. Out came
others with boxes full of bottles
of milk.

Mr. March was going home to
dinner. He stopped his truck and
helped carry things out of the market.

"Help me carry out the peaches and
apples," called a man.

Mr. March ran to help carry peaches
and apples and other fruits.

Before long, a big red fire truck
came to the fire. One of the firemen
made all the people get out
of the market.

"You must all get out of here,"
he said. "Keep away from the fire
so the firemen can do their work."

Some firemen got a large machine.
They used the machine to throw water
on the fire.

"Hurrah!" shouted all the people.
"Hurrah for the firemen!"

One of the firemen waved his hand.

"This is not very much of a fire,"
he said. "We will have this fire out
soon."

A man wanted to go into the market.

"Oh, don't go in there," said one
of the firemen. "You had better keep
away. The firemen will tell you when
the fire is out."

"Oh dear!" said the man. "My cat
is in there. I can hear her cry.
I wish you would let me get her."

"Just tell me where your pet is,"
said one of the firemen. "I will get
the cat myself. You wait here."

Soon he came out with the cat.

"Here is your pet cat," he said. "At first I thought she did not want to come with me. When I tried to take her out of her bed, she went f-ff-t, f-ff-t."

"Thank you very much," said the man. "I like this cat. Some people wanted to buy Niki today, but I would not sell her. I want to keep her myself. I like her better than any other pet."

When the fire was out, Mr. March
got into his truck. He could not
make the truck go.

He saw Tim Camp in the big yellow
dairy wagon. Mr. March called to Tim.

"I have been helping at the fire,"
said Mr. March. "I guess water got
into my truck. Now I cannot make
it go."

"You cannot leave your truck
in the street all night," said Tim.

"Right now Blackie and I have no
work of our own to do. We are just
going to the barn. We have time
enough to help a friend, don't we,
Blackie?"

"The truck may weigh too much
for him to pull," said Mr. March.

"We shall see about that," said Tim. "Blackie might do better than you think he will. Blackie, show our neighbor what a good horse can do."

Blackie pulled the truck to one side of the street.

"I knew he could do it," said Tim.

"Well, Billy said that Blackie was the best horse in town. I think so myself, now," said Mr. March.

Yellow Chick
and
Other Animals

Little Yellow Chick

Yellow Chick was near some water. He wanted to cross the water, but he did not know how to do it.

Yellow Chick tried and tried, but he could not cross the water. He began to cry.

"Oh, oh," he said. "I want to cross the water. I cannot cross. Oh, oh!"

Before long Waddling Duck came by. He saw Yellow Chick. He waddled over to the water.

"What makes you cry, Yellow Chick?" asked Waddling Duck.

Yellow Chick answered, "I am crying
because I cannot cross the puddle
of water."

"Oh, I will tell you how to cross
the puddle," said Waddling Duck.
"Swim like I do."

Waddling Duck sat down in the
water. He made his feet go up
and down.

Yellow Chick said, "I cannot swim
because I do not have feet like yours."

Waddling Duck did not know how
to help. He made his wings go up
and down. Flap, flap went his wings.

Just then a bird flew to the puddle.
She heard Yellow Chick cry. The bird
saw Waddling Duck flap his wings.

"Why do you cry, Yellow Chick?"
asked Warbling Wren. "Are you
crying because you cannot cross
the puddle?"

"Yes," answered the little chick.
"Can you tell me how to cross?"

"Well, every chicken has wings,"
said Warbling Wren. "Flap your
wings as fast as you can. You will
go up over the puddle. That is how
you can cross."

Flap, flap, flap went Yellow Chick's wings. Then he began to cry again because he could not fly.

"My wings are not like yours," said Yellow Chick. "Oh, oh, oh! This is just awful. I cannot cross the puddle. I cannot fly."

Warbling Wren flew over the puddle. She flew back again.

"Oh, oh, oh!" said Warbling Wren. "This is awful! This is just awful! We cannot do a thing to help Yellow Chick."

Yellow Chick Gets Help

Just then Bouncing Bunny came by
the puddle.

"What is just awful?" he asked.
"Why are you crying, Yellow Chick?"

"I am crying because I cannot go
across the puddle," answered the chick.
"I cannot swim. I tried to flap
my wings, but I cannot fly."

"Well, why do you not jump across
the puddle?" asked Bouncing Bunny.
"See me do it."

"You can jump because you have very long legs," said Yellow Chick. "My legs are not long. I cannot jump across."

"Oh, oh," said Bouncing Bunny. "This is awful. Your legs will not help you cross the puddle."

"Oh, yes, they will," said a bug that was in the grass. "I can tell him how his legs will help him."

"How can his legs help him?" asked the animals. "You tell us, Black Bug."

"Yellow Chick can walk around the puddle," said Black Bug.

Yellow Chick said, "That is not so hard to do. Why did I not think of that before?"

Then all the animals were happy. Waddling Duck began to swim and Warbling Wren flew over the puddle. Bouncing Bunny jumped across it.

Yellow Chick and his good friend, Black Bug, just walked around the puddle.

The Animal Party

There was going to be a party.
Many animals had been invited to it.
Yellow Chick knew that his friend
Black Bug had not been invited.
He told Waddling Duck about it.

"I wish that we could invite him,"
said Yellow Chick. "He is my good
friend. I would like to take him
to the party."

"Black Bug may be a fine friend,
but he is small," said Waddling Duck.
"I think he is much too small to go
to a party with big animals."

Just then Big Dog came along.

"Who is too small?" he asked.

"Black Bug is too small," the duck
told Big Dog. "He is a fine friend.
But he is not big enough to be invited
to our party."

"You are right," said Big Dog.
"He is much too small to go along.
It would be too hard to take him."

Then Big Dog began to laugh.

"Your queer little friend does not have the right clothes for a party," said Big Dog. "He does not have a fine coat like I have. I don't see how he keeps from being very cold."

"I wish he could have new clothes," said Yellow Chick. "He would look fine in a yellow coat like I have."

"I always have fine white clothes," said Waddling Duck. "I have pretty legs and feet, too."

"I think a black coat is best,"
said Big Dog. "I like black legs and
feet. The legs must be strong, too.
I do not see how any animal can get
along without strong legs."

"My legs are strong and I can swim
with them," said Waddling Duck.

"They may be all right for a duck,"
said Big Dog. "For myself, I like legs
that are strong enough to take me
any place."

Just then the animals heard a bird fly over them. It was Warbling Wren. She came to rest near the animals.

Yellow Chick told Warbling Wren about wanting to invite Black Bug to the party.

"Black Bug is a good friend, but he is very small," said Yellow Chick. "I guess he is too small to go."

"I am small, too, but I am going to the party," said Warbling Wren.

"We should not invite Black Bug because he does not have fine clothes," said Waddling Duck.

"He does not have any wings," said Warbling Wren. "He cannot fly without them. I do not know how he can go any place at all."

Mr. Donkey

Along came Mr. Donkey. When he saw all the other animals he stopped to rest. He told the animals about how hard he had to work.

"You should see the way I work," he said. "I do not know how people would get along without a donkey to help them. It is a good thing I am a strong animal.

Now I must take a little rest before I go to the party."

The donkey went over near some bushes and took a rest.

Yellow Chick went over to the place
where Mr. Donkey was resting.
He told the donkey about Black Bug.

"Mr. Donkey, do you think my
friend should be invited to our party?"
asked Yellow Chick.

"He should not be invited because
he is too small," said the donkey.
"He is not very strong. He never
does any hard work. His only coat
is an old black one. He would look
very queer at a party with old clothes."

Big Dog looked very cross.

"That is no way to talk," he said.
"A black coat is just as good
as any other."

"It may be all right for an animal like you because you are only a pet. You never work," said Mr. Donkey.

Mr. Donkey looked at Warbling Wren and the other animals.

"I don't see why you should talk about Black Bug," he said. "You do not try to work. I am the only one here who does any hard work."

Black Bug Comes Along

The animals had not seen the bug for a long time. Now they saw him coming.

"I cannot go on without a rest," he said. "I will sit here and talk with you."

Mr. Donkey asked, "Why do you have to rest, Black Bug?"

"It is because I work so hard," answered Black Bug.

The little bug told the animals about his work.

"I try to keep bad bugs out of the gardens and fields," he said. "I try to keep bad bugs out of trees, too."

Black Bug looked up at the trees.

He said, "I took many bad bugs out of these trees. That is why these trees are so big now. And they give animals a fine place to rest on these warm days.

"Watch me. I will show you the way I do my work on these large trees."

Up, up went the little bug. He took many bad bugs out of the tree.

"Come up here so you can see the way I do it," he said.

"I could fly up, but there would be no place to sit," said the wren. "I might fall off if I tried to sit where Black Bug is working."

Waddling Duck and Yellow Chick made their wings flap.

"We cannot get far off the ground with these wings," said Waddling Duck. "We cannot see a thing."

"I will try to get up there," said Big Dog.

He jumped and jumped, but he could not get near Black Bug.

Mr. Donkey got up. He put up his head as far as it would go.

"That is very queer," he said. "That little bug can sit up there where I cannot watch him."

"I could not get off the ground,"
said little Yellow Chick. "Black Bug
is the only one who can get up
on that tree."

"We are fine ones to sit and talk
about him," little Warbling Wren told
the other animals. "He can do things
that not any of us can do."

"Yes, you are right," said Big Dog. "We should not talk about his clothes. That black coat may not be warm, but it looks very fine."

"I never saw small legs that were so strong. They can go up a tree so fast," the wren told the others. "It took Black Bug no time at all to get up there. He could find a place to sit, too. He did not fall off the tree."

"Black Bug works very hard, too," said Mr. Donkey. "He does many things to help people. We did not know these things before. We should invite him to our party."

"Hurrah!" shouted Yellow Chick. "I am glad my friend can come along with us."

"I will carry him to the party," said Big Dog. "He can sit on my back. I would not think of going to the party without him."

So off went the little black bug with the other animals. They had a fine time at the party.

The Animals Want a Home

One time there was a sheep who wanted a new home. He wanted another animal to live with him.

First the sheep went to the pig.

"Friend pig, it would be fine to have our own home," he said. "Let us try to make a warm home in the woods."

The pig said that he would be glad
to build a fine warm home. So the pig
and the sheep went off to the woods.

On the road they saw a goose.

"Good day," said the goose. "Where
are you good people going?"

"We are on our way to the woods.
We are going to build a new home,"
said the sheep.

"I think I shall go along with you,"
the goose told the other animals.
"I can help build the home. All of us
can live in it."

"What can a goose do to help?"
asked the sheep.

"Oh, I can pick up old leaves,"
answered the goose. "If old leaves
are stuffed in places around the house,
they will help keep us warm."

"Very well, then," said the sheep.
"If you want to help build a house,
you may come with us. We will live
together."

Off the animals went to find
a place for their home.

Before very long they met a rabbit.

"Good day," said the brown rabbit.
"Where are you going?"

"We are all going to the woods
to build a house," answered the pig.

"It is a good thing you met me,"
said the rabbit. "See these paws?
They are strong. I will try to help
you build a house. It will be better
if we work together."

"If you want to work hard, you are
invited to come along," said the pig.

Away went the sheep and the pig
and the goose and the rabbit.

They Build the Home

Next the animals met a hen and a rooster.

"Good day," crowed the big rooster. "Where are you going this fine day?"

"We are off to the woods to find a place to build a warm house," answered the goose.

"Oh, it is a good thing you met us," said the rooster. "We should go along with you. The hen and I get up early in the morning. I can crow, so you will get up in time to do your work. You cannot get along without me."

"Come along then," said the goose. "We don't want to sleep when there is work to be done."

The hen told the animals that she would help the goose. The animals invited her to go along with them.

All the animals worked together to build their house.

The rooster crowed every morning to make the animals get up early.

The pig dug up ground near trees. He made the trees fall.

Then the sheep took all the trees to the rabbit. The rabbit pushed the trees into place.

The goose and the hen picked up leaves from the ground. They stuffed the leaves here and stuffed them there to make the house warm. They stuffed leaves into every place that they could find.

Soon the animals had a fine warm house ready.

"We must have a garden, if we are going to live here," said the sheep. "We cannot get along without food."

The pig dug and dug. The hen and the rooster put seeds into the ground. The rabbit and the sheep helped the other animals.

"Now we have a house and a garden of our own," said the sheep. "We all helped each other. We can rest now. I know we will be happy together."

Tim Wants a Pet

Tim lived in a big town. He had many stuffed animals to play with, but he had no pet. Tim wanted a pet of his own.

One day Tim and his daddy took a walk. Tim saw a horse.

"I like horses," said Tim. "But I guess a horse is too big for a pet."

Daddy said, "You have been invited to go to the country. You may see a small animal there that you would like for a pet."

When Tim went to the country,
Uncle Jack met him at the train.

"This has been a very warm day,"
said Uncle Jack. "You have come
a long way. You can rest first.
Then put on your old clothes and
I will show you the farm animals."

"Oh, I don't have to rest,"
said Tim. "I will get ready now."

Soon Tim and Uncle Jack went off
together to see the farm animals.

When they were only a little way from the house, they heard a boy calling.

"Well, here comes Billy Hard," said Uncle Jack. "Billy is one of our neighbors. I told him you would come today. You and Billy will have good times together."

Billy told Tim about pets he had at the farm. One pet was a sheep.

"I do not have any pet," said Tim.

"Oh, that is too bad," said Billy. "We will try to get one for you."

Just then Tim saw a big rooster. Near it was a mother hen and her little chicks.

"One of these chicks would be a fine pet," said Tim.

"You could not take the chick away from its mother," said Billy. "It does not know how to get its food. These chicks are too little to get along without their mother."

The rooster began to flap its big wings. Tim asked if the rooster was going to fly.

"He cannot fly," answered Billy. "He is just going to crow."

The boys saw a big goose looking
around in the grass. Billy told Tim
that the goose was looking for bugs.

"I could find bugs in our garden
for that goose," said Tim. "But I
don't think I would like the goose
for a pet."

Just then Uncle Jack told Tim
to look at something in the garden.

Tim saw a big rabbit. It dug
up a vegetable and began to eat.

"A bunny would be a good pet
for you," said Billy.

"I think I will get that one,"
said Tim.

But when Tim got near the garden
the rabbit saw him. Away it went,
bouncing across the road on its
strong legs.

"I guess that rabbit does not
want to live in town," said Tim.

The next morning Tim went to see
the pigs. All the little pigs were
in a puddle of water.

"They are funny and I like them,"
said Tim. "But I could not have
a pig in our yard."

Uncle Jack laughed and laughed.

"I think your mother would be
surprised if you came home
with a pig," he said.

Tim heard a noise. He saw some ducks waddling to a little lake.

"Quack, quack," said the ducks.

"I guess those ducks are talking to each other," said Tim. "Do they swim every day?"

"Yes, all ducks must have a place to swim," answered Uncle Jack.

"Then I cannot take a duck home with me," said Tim. "There is no lake near our house."

"I think I know where we can get a pet for you," said Uncle Jack. "And we will get it today."

Uncle Jack got his car. Then he
and Tim went to another farm.

A man at the farm showed Tim
three little dogs.

"You may have the one you like
best," he said.

Tim did not know what he should
do because he liked all the dogs.
He just wanted to sit and look
at all three of them.

Just then one little dog saw Tim.
Its tail began to go fast. It went
to Tim and began to bark.

"Why did he bark?" asked Tim.

"The dog likes you," said the man.

So Tim took the little brown dog.

"Oh, I am so glad to have you,"
said Tim. "I will build a house
for you. I never will be cross
with you. We will have good times
at Uncle Jack's. We will have fun
when we go home, too."

Then Tim thanked the man and
he thanked Uncle Jack, too.

"Now I have a pet and I am so
happy," said Tim.

"Bow wow," said the little dog.

"I guess the dog is happy, too,"
said Uncle Jack.

Fun with Mary and Jim

The New Calf

Mary Winters was asleep. Her
brother Jim called to her.

"Mary, Mary," he called. "Get up!"

Mary sat up in her bed. She looked
at her brother.

"It cannot be morning," she said.
"It is not light."

Mary heard the roosters crowing.

"The roosters are not asleep,"
she said. "I guess it is morning, but
it is too early to get up."

"Daddy just told me that our cow has a new calf," said Jim. "The one who gets to the barn first can have the calf for a present."

"Oh," said Mary, as she jumped out of bed. "I am so glad you told me. I want that calf for my own."

Mary put on her clothes as fast as she could. Her brother Jim got his clothes on first. Soon the children were off to the barn.

Who Gets the Present?

A calf was asleep near its mother.
The cow was licking her baby.

"Look," said Mary. "She is licking
the calf just like the mother cat
licks Kitty. Does a mother cow
always do that, Daddy?"

"Yes," answered Daddy. "A cow
always licks a new calf that way.
That is the way she washes the calf."

Just then the calf got up. It could
hardly stand. Mary and Jim laughed
when they saw how funny it looked
on its wobbly legs.

"Who got here first to see the calf?"
asked Mr. Winters.

"Jim did," answered Mary. "I guess
he gets the present. What will you
name the calf?"

"I think I will call it Wobbly
because it has wobbly little legs,"
answered Jim.

Mary asked Jim to let her feed
the calf. Jim told her that the cow
would feed her baby.

"The cow always feeds her calf
at first," said Jim. "The little calf
is going to have breakfast now."

Jim and Mary watched the calf have
its breakfast. Then their father
told them it was time for children
to have breakfast, too.

"I always like to eat," said Jim.
"But I am not hungry this morning.
Please let me watch our new calf
for a while."

"A boy must have plenty to eat,"
said Jim's father. "Eat breakfast
first. Then come back to the barn
and watch your calf."

"All right," said Jim. "It will take
hardly any time to eat.

"Good-by, Wobbly. I will be right
back as soon as I eat my breakfast."

A Present for Mary

One morning while Mary was eating breakfast, her father came in. He told her some nice news.

He said that a present was waiting for her.

"We have some new little pigs down in the pen," he said. "I want you to see them right after breakfast. You can pick the one you like best."

"How nice," said Mary. "I am going to have a little pig of my very own. I can hardly wait to see the pigs. Please let me see them right away."

Mrs. Winters said Mary did not have
to wash dishes that morning.

As soon as breakfast was over,
Mary ran to the pen. She wanted
to see the seven little pigs.

Mother pig was asleep. All seven
of the pigs were eating.

After one pig had plenty to eat,
it waddled away from its mother.
Mary laughed when she saw it walk
on its short legs.

"All seven of the pigs are nice,"
she said. "I will take that one.
It looks so funny walking around
on its short legs."

While Mary was watching the seven little pigs, Jim came to the pen. Mary showed him her own small pig.

"Please help me think of a name for it," said Mary.

"Your pig is small," said her brother. "You will have to give it a short name."

"You are right," said Mary. "I know a short name for a small pig. I will call it Tiny.

That is just the right kind of name for a tiny pig."

Daddy told the children there were
many things to learn about the care
of their pets.

"You must be kind to the calf,"
he told Jim. "The cow cannot always
feed it. You must learn what to feed
the calf. You must wash it, too."

"Soon the mother pig will stop
feeding Tiny," Daddy said to Mary.
"You will have to give the pig plenty
to eat. Tiny must have a warm place
to sleep, too."

"We will learn how to take care
of our pets," said the children.
"We will always be kind to them."

Wobbly Grows Up

Jim's calf began to grow. His legs were growing long and they were not wobbly any more.

The little calf liked to run around the yard. He liked to play with Spot. Wobbly and Spot always had fine times together.

One time Spot was asleep in the yard. Wobbly wanted to play with the dog. Spot wanted to sleep.

Jim and Mary watched Wobbly to see what he would do.

Wobbly swished his tail, but Spot did not look up. The calf kicked up his feet. Spot kept very still. He did not look up.

Wobbly began to lick Spot's face. Spot could not keep still. He got up.

Away went Wobbly. Away went Spot after the calf. Up and down the yard they ran.

Jim laughed when he saw the dog and the calf playing together. He talked to Mary about them.

"That calf never wants to keep still," said Jim. "When he sees Spot any place, he always goes there. Spot will learn that he can hardly find a place to sleep when Wobbly wants to play."

"I guess Wobbly knows Spot never likes to have his face washed that way," said Mary. "He always licks Spot's face when he wants to make the dog get up."

"Well, I guess Spot likes to play with the calf," said Jim. "He always goes with the calf. He is always kind to Wobbly, too."

One day Jim got a small pail and went to the calf's pen. He wanted Wobbly to learn how to drink milk from a pail.

"The cow cannot always feed you," said Jim. "You are growing up now. You must learn to drink from a pail."

Jim washed his hands. Then he put plenty of milk in the pail. He put one hand into the milk.

"Here, Wobbly," he said. "You can lick the nice milk off my hands."

Wobbly licked the milk off Jim's hand. He did it again and again.

Then Jim put his hand way down into the pail. Wobbly kept on licking Jim's hand.

Soon Jim took his hand out of the pail. The calf kept on drinking the milk.

"I knew you would learn how to drink from a pail," said Jim. "I will hold the pail for you. Now I can take care of you all the time."

Then Jim laughed and said, "Wobbly, you have milk all over your nose."

142

Wobbly and the Pail

Once when Wobbly was drinking milk, he put his nose way down in the pail. He wanted to get all the milk that was at the bottom of the pail.

All at once the calf pushed his nose on the bottom of the pail. Then, up went his head.

Jim tried to hold on to the pail, but the calf began to back away.

"There goes the pail," said Jim. "There goes the rest of the milk."

Down ran the milk. It went all over the calf.

The calf kept backing away from Jim.
He kicked and kicked. He did not know
how to get the pail off his head.

"Stop kicking," said Jim. "The pail
is caught on your head. You never can
get the pail off your head by kicking
your feet like that. I never have seen
a calf like you. I cannot hold you.
Please stand still while I try to take
the pail off."

Jim got the pail off Wobbly's head.
He had to laugh when he saw the
funny look on the calf's face.

"That is once you had a surprise,"
said Jim. "I think you could get
plenty of milk without being so greedy.
You should not put your head down
to the bottom of the pail.

"Don't be so greedy when I feed you.
Then you will not be caught that way."

Then Jim laughed again and said,
"I am glad we were not in the barn.
I would have to wash the floor."

Funny Little Pig

Mary was in the yard. All at once she heard a noise in her playhouse.

Bang! A box of doll clothes hit the floor of the playhouse.

Bang! A pail hit the floor.

Mary did not know what had happened. She ran to the playhouse. Who should be there but Tiny. The pig was banging a little pail upon the floor.

"How do you happen to be there,"
asked Mary. "You should not be out
of your pen."

Tiny had her funny nose way down
at the bottom of a small pail.
She just kept banging the small pail
upon the floor.

Bang, bang went the little pail,
as Tiny ran around in the playhouse.

"I never have seen such a greedy
pig," said Mary. "You always get
plenty of food, but you never have
enough."

Mary caught the little pig and
took it back to its pen.

"You are growing fast," said Mary.
"You were such a small pig when I got
you for a present. You are different
now. Tiny, soon you will be so big
that I will not be able to carry you.
I can hardly do it now."

Then Mary laughed.

"You will be so big you will not be
able to go under your pen," she said.
"Then you cannot get away like you
did today."

All summer Mary took good care
of Tiny. She gave the pig many
different kinds of vegetables to eat.
Mary gave Tiny plenty of milk
to drink.

Tiny was growing fast. She was
always hungry. She never was able
to find enough to eat.

"Every morning and night I bring
plenty of food for you," said Mary.
"You never get enough. I think
you are a greedy little pig."

When the pig looked up at Mary,
it made her laugh.

"You are such a funny little pig,"
said Mary. "Even if you are greedy,
you still are a fine pig."

When fall came, Tiny was too big
to get out of her pen. If she tried
to get out, she always got caught
under the pen. Once in a while, Mary
let Tiny out for a short walk.

"Once she got into the garden,"
Mary told Jim. "I caught her, but
I could not even hold her. Spot had
to help bring her back."

"Tiny wants to eat what she sees,"
said Jim. "She even tried to eat my
ball. A ball would be a funny kind
of food for a pig."

When winter came, there was snow
and ice all over the ground. Jim and
Mary liked to slide on the ice.

Once Tiny watched Jim and Mary
slide on the ice. The pig sat down
upon the ice. She put out her feet.
She began to slide on the ice, too.

"Oh, what a fine trick," said Mary.
"Tiny is even funny enough to be
a clown. She should be in a circus."

The Pet Goose

Every spring there were baby geese at the farm. They all waddled around in the grass after their mother. They were always looking for bugs to eat.

There was one small goose that Mary liked best of all. Mary caught many, many different kinds of bugs to feed the little goose.

Before long the goose ran to Mary every time it heard her in the yard. It thought Mary would bring something to eat.

"I guess you know that I always bring something good for you to eat," said Mary. "You are a nice little pet. I must think of a nice name for you."

While Mary was thinking, the goose saw a frog in the grass. It never had seen a frog before. It thought the frog was a big green bug.

The goose looked at the green frog for a while. Just as it was ready to take the green frog in its mouth, something happened.

The green frog jumped upon a stone.
The goose did not know what it should
do. It was afraid of the frog.

"S-s-s-s, S-s-s-s," said the goose.
"S-s-s-s, S-s-s-s," it said again.

"What happened?" asked Mary.

Then she saw the little green frog
jumping around in the grass.

"Don't be afraid of it," said Mary.
"That is just a little green frog.
When you grow up you will be able
to catch frogs."

While the green frog was jumping,
the little goose kept looking at it.

"S-s-s-s, S-s-s-s," said the goose.

"Well, you did not have to grow up
to learn to make that kind of noise,"
said Mary. "I will call you Siz.
That will be a fine name for you.

"Come with me, Siz. I will get
something for you to eat."

Once Mother goose was walking
around in the green grass with her
seven geese. While the geese were
in the yard, Siz heard Mary near the
playhouse. Siz started off to see her.

Spot saw the little goose start
to go to the playhouse. He thought
Siz should stay with the other geese.
Spot ran to the little goose.

The goose saw Spot in its way.

"S-s-s-s, S-s-s-s," said the goose.

Spot did not get out of the way.

He barked and barked at the goose.

When the goose heard the noise,
it was afraid. It started to run
to its mother. Spot ran after it.

Mother goose had heard Spot barking.
She had seen him run after her baby.

The big goose put out her wings and
started to run.

"S-s-s-s, S-s-s-s," she said.

Spot saw the big goose coming.
That was enough for him. He was
afraid of those big wings. He did
not stay in her way. He started
to run as fast as he could.

Then the mother goose went back
to her seven little geese. She was
holding her head up. She wanted
the geese to know they should never
be afraid while she was there.

Ready for Market

Mr. Winters was going to town
in the big truck. He was going to take
different kinds of vegetables to sell
at the market. He was going to take
eggs and chickens to sell, too.

After breakfast, Jim told his father
that he would help get the eggs ready.

"Fine," said Mr. Winters. "You can
begin work right now. I will be able
to help after I feed and milk the cow."

"When Daddy goes to market, I am
going with him," Jim told Wobbly.
"I will stay there just a short time.
You play with Spot. Be a good calf."

Mother gave Jim a big green pail.
She asked him if he would carry it
to the pen.

"Please take this down to the pen,"
said Mrs. Winters. "The pigs should
have their breakfast now."

Jim took the big pail to the pen.
When the seven pigs heard him coming,
they started to make an awful noise.

Jim laughed when he heard them.

"You are able to make plenty of noise
for such small pigs," he said. "I guess
every one of you is as greedy as Tiny."

The pigs kept on with the noise.

"Keep still," said Jim. "I will
bring your breakfast just as soon
as I can. I never have seen such
greedy pigs."

All at once the mother hog pushed
the seven little pigs out of her way.
She ran to the pail and hit the bottom
of it with her head.

The pail turned over and the food
came down upon the little pigs.
They had not seen the pail turn over.
They did not know what had happened.
The pigs started to run different ways.
One of them almost made Jim fall down.

"My, my," said Jim. "Even you are greedy, Mother hog. How can the baby pigs learn to be nice when they see you do that. You want them to grow up to be nice pigs, don't you?"

The mother hog never looked up. She did not care what her pigs did so long as she was able to get enough food. She just kept on eating her breakfast.

While Jim was feeding the pigs,
Mary heard Father tell her brother
they might sell some geese.

"If Father is going to take geese
to the market, he might take Siz,"
thought Mary. "That will never do."

Mary saw Siz looking for frogs. She
took the goose behind the house.
She put Siz into a big green box.

"You stay there, Siz," said Mary.
"Don't make any noise. Keep still
so you will not be caught. We don't
want Daddy to sell you at the market."

Father had been washing vegetables
to take to market. He was ready
to put them into the green box.

"S-s-s-s," said something that was
in the box. "S-s-s-s, S-s-s-s."

"How did you get into this box,"
asked Mr. Winters.

"I put her in the box," said Mary.
"I told her to stay there. I did it
because I was afraid you would sell
my little pet."

"Hardly any one would want to buy
such a little goose," said her daddy.
"The goose was a present to you.
I never will sell your pet."

Books and Pets

New Books

All of the children were in school.
It was almost time for work to begin.

Before they started their lessons,
the children had many things to do.
Some boys put water on tiny gardens
that were in boxes. Some girls gave
food to the bird.

Then Miss Day told the children
she had a nice surprise for them.
She opened a big box and took out
some books.

"Oh, some new books," said Billy.
"Are they story books?"

"These new books are about pets,"
answered Miss Day. "The first story
is about rabbits. Would you like
to read it today?"

"Yes, yes," answered the children.

Billy and Don helped give books
to the children. All the boys and
girls looked at the books.

Don said, "Look, a rabbit is out
of its pen! Something will happen
to it. May we read about it now?"

Miss Day let all the children read
to learn what happened to the rabbit.
The children liked the story.

The Rabbit Family

"I have two rabbits," said Don.
"I can bring them to school."

"We will have to build a pen
for them," said Sally.

Miss Day said that the children
could build a pen. Then Don could
bring his rabbits to school.

The boys and girls worked hard
to make a place to put the rabbits.
Soon the pen was ready. There was
a little house in the pen.

Don made a little sign. It said:

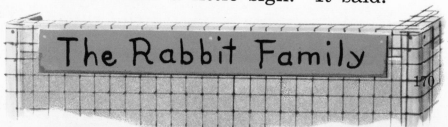

The Rabbit Family

The next day Don brought his pets
to school. He told the children how
he took care of the rabbits.

"They like carrots," he said. "They
eat carrots and other vegetables."

"That is just like the rabbit family
we are reading about in our books,"
said Sally. "There are many carrots
in our little gardens. Just as soon
as those carrots grow big enough,
we can feed them to the rabbits."

"Do your rabbits have names?"
asked Betty.

"No, but we can name the rabbits
while they are here," answered Don.

All the children helped take care
of the rabbit family. They kept the pen
clean. They brought fresh clean grass
for the pen every morning.

Some boys and girls brought carrots.
Other children brought different kinds
of vegetables for the pets.

One morning Sally was watching
one of the rabbits eat a carrot.
She laughed at the way his nose
went up and down.

"His nose is twitchy," said Sally.
"Twitchy Nose would be a good name
for this rabbit. We could just call him
Twitchy.

"The other one has a twitchy nose,
but look at her tail. She has only
a puff for a tail. We can name
her Puff."

"I think those are good names,"
said Don. "I will call my rabbits
Puff and Twitchy."

Puff Gives Don a Surprise

One day the children were ready
to put clean grass in the pen.
They had carrots for the rabbits, too.

Everyone saw Twitchy in the pen.
Don looked into the house to see Puff.
He shouted to the children.

"Everyone come here!" shouted Don.
"There is a big family now."

The children looked into the house
and saw five tiny rabbits. The babies
had very short ears. Their tiny tails
hardly showed at all.

Everyone stood near the house and watched Puff feed her babies.

When the babies were through eating, they went to sleep.

"Now we can have our reading lesson," said Miss Day. "After that we will look at Puff and her babies again."

"May we get our new books? We would like to read about other pets today," said Don.

Pets at School

One story was about a little hen. The children liked the little red hen because she worked so hard.

When all the boys and girls were through reading, Sally told them about her pet hen.

"She is not a red hen," said Sally. "She is light brown, so I named her Sandy."

Then everyone talked about pets. Sally asked if she could bring Sandy to school.

"Everyone may bring pets to school," said Miss Day. "All the pets may come on the same day. Each of you must take care of your own pet."

Many different pets came to school.
There were two dogs and a pretty cat.
Sandy, the brown hen, was there, too.

Billy brought his two white mice.
Their names were Skip and Toots.
The mice were in the same cage.

Tom brought a turtle. The turtle
was in a cage, too. There was a dish
of water at the bottom of the cage.

Everyone wanted to know if any pets
could do tricks. Some children said
their pets could do them.

"Sandy cannot do any tricks,"
said Sally. "She will just stay
in her basket."

Jack showed the children a trick
that his dog could do.

"Barky can find a ball," said Jack.
"I will put my hands over his eyes.
Barky will not be able to see where
you put the ball, but he will find
it just the same."

Jack put his hands over Barky's eyes.
Sally got a ball. Then she walked
over to some books.

Barky kept very still. He put up
his ears. Then Sally put the ball
behind the books.

Jack took his hands off Barky's eyes.
"Bow wow," said the dog.

Away he went to find the ball.

Barky found the ball right away and took it in his mouth. Then he ran to Jack with the ball.

Everyone clapped when Barky found the ball. The children wanted Barky to do the same trick over and over again. They put their hands over Barky's eyes. They put the ball in different places in the room. Barky found it every time.

"Could he smell it?" asked Ann. "Is that how he found the ball?"

"I think I know how he found it," said Don. "Barky heard us walk to the places we put the ball."

When Barky was through his trick, Jim called his dog. He wanted Rex to do a trick for the children.

Rex stood up on two feet. Around and around he went. Everyone clapped for Rex, too.

"That was fine," said Jack. "I will show Barky how to do that same trick. It will be fun to train him."

"Your pets may rest for a while," said Miss Day. "You can make pictures of your pets. If you do not have a pet, make a picture of one you would like to have."

"Our lessons will not seem hard after we had so much fun," said Don.

Something Funny Happened

The children talked about how they took care of their own pets.

Billy told how he made the cage for his white mice.

"I keep the cage clean," he said. "Every morning I put clean paper on the bottom of the cage. The paper keeps the cage clean. White mice like to live in a nice clean place. My pets seem to keep me busy every morning."

"We put paper in the bird's cage, too," said Betty. "Sally and I put clean paper in the cage this morning."

Sally asked Tom if he put paper in the turtle's cage.

"No, I never put paper in its cage," answered Tom. "The turtle seems to like to walk on grass and stones.

A pan of water is inside the cage. The turtle likes to swim in it.

Every day I take some of the water out of the pan. I always put in some fresh water. As soon as I put the pan inside the cage, my turtle takes a swim. He is in the pan now."

The boys and girls went to the back of the room to see the turtle swim. They stood and watched Tom's pet.

Jane stood near the rabbit family.
She saw Twitchy going in and out
of the little house.

"Twitchy seems to be busy going
in and out of the house," said Jane.
"There may be something inside the
house that Twitchy does not like. I
will look inside and see what it is."

When Jane looked inside the house
Puff had all her babies behind her.
In front of Puff there was a little
white animal. Two tiny pink eyes
looked up at Jane.

"Oh," said Jane. "I found one
of the mice right in front of Puff.
She seems to be afraid of it."

Billy ran to the cage where he kept
the mice. Both the mice were out.

"They both got out the same place,"
said Billy. "Jack, you get the one
in the rabbit house. We will look
for the other one."

"Those mice can climb up on things,"
said Don. "We will have to look all
over the room."

"I will get my cat," said Betty.
"She must not find your pet."

Just then Sandy began to make
an awful noise.

"Cluck, cluck, cluck," said the hen.

"Why is Sandy making so much
noise?" asked Sally.

Sally and Jane ran to see Sandy.

The hen was in her basket. In front
of her was an animal with pink eyes.

"We have found your pet," said Sally.
"It climbed inside Sandy's basket.
Sandy does not like mice. That is why
she was making so much noise."

"Cluck, cluck, cluck," said Sandy.

Soon Billy had both the mice back inside their cage.

"They will not climb out again," said Billy.

"The pets have kept us very busy today," said Miss Day. "It was nice to have them at school. Now you may take them home. Take home the pictures you made, too."

"The pets seem to like our school," said Jack. "We all had a good time."

Making Animals

One day there was a big machine in front of the school. It was just outside the yard. Some men were near the machine.

The machine dug into the ground. The children stopped to watch it.

"That machine has a big mouth," said Jack. "It puts its big mouth into the ground. When it comes up, the mouth will be full."

Down went the big mouth. When it came up, it was full.

Don ran outside the playground.
He wanted to talk to the men.

"Look out!" said one of the men.
"You will slide in that clay."

"Is that clay?" asked Don. "May we
have some? We can use it to make
clay animals."

"We will get some clay for you,"
answered one of the men. "We will
get enough clay for all the children.

"The boys and girls had better stay
inside the playground. We will put
the clay inside the playground, too.
You can make things there."

"That is fine," said Don. "Miss Day
does not want any of us to play outside
the playground. She does not want us
to go near that big machine."

Soon the children were busy making clay animals. Before they were through, it was time for school to begin.

The children went into their room. They told Miss Day about the nice clay that the men gave them. They told her about the clay animals.

"Bring them inside if you wish," said Miss Day.

"Those men will bring some clay in here," said Don. "Here is a pan they can use for it."

"We need plenty of clay," said Tom. "Don can take the pan. I found a bag. Now the men can bring in all we need."

Both boys went outside to get clay. One of the men brought it in for them.

Miss Day found some paper. She put it on a big table.

"We need the paper to keep our table clean," she said. "You may put the bag of clay at one end of the table. Put the pan at the other end."

"We cannot all make clay animals at the same time," said Sally.

"I know what we can do," said Mary. "Some of us can read a story about pets. Then we can make the pets out of clay."

"It was nice of those men to give us the clay," said Betty. "When I was out on the playground, I could not think of what to make. But now I can."

"We are going to read about pets," said Jane. "After we read, I will think of something to make, too."

Miss Day stood near the table and watched the busy children. She saw Billy making a funny nose for a dog. She saw Jane cut pink paper to make eyes for some mice.

Jane said, "All white mice should have pink eyes. These mice are just babies, but I am going to paint them white."

"I am making a monkey," said Don. "I will put both his front feet on one end of a stick. Then he will be ready to climb.

First I have to cut a stick. I need some paint for it, too."

"You seem to know just what to do," said Miss Day.

Jack cut out two big paper ears
to put on an elephant. He made a ball
of clay on the end of its trunk.

"Look at this elephant, Miss Day,"
said Jack. "I will paint the elephant.
I can put it in a bag to carry it home."

"I am making two skunks," said Lee.

Soon all the clay animals were done.
The children made a parade of
animals on the big table.

"It was fun making them," said Ann.
"When we go outside, I will see those
men. I will tell the men how much fun
we had with the clay they gave us."

Party Plans

The boys and girls had been reading about different animals. They asked Miss Day if they could have an animal party.

Miss Day asked if the children had any plans for the party.

"We thought it would be fun to dress like animals," said Ann.

"That would be fun," said Miss Day. "There are many things we need to do if we are to have a party. We must plan how we want our room to look. We must plan games for the party."

"We need something to eat, too," said Billy.

"Would you like to draw the animals you want to be?" asked Miss Day.

"Oh, that will be fun," said Sally. "We can draw pictures and put them around the room. Then we can see how each one is going to dress."

"Then not all of us will be dressed the same way," said Jack. "I am going to draw the picture of a big rooster. That is what I will be at the party. May we draw the pictures now?"

Miss Day told the children that they should make plans first. They should know what each one had to do.

The children made plans for games.
They talked about how to dress.

"Some of us know songs about
animals," said Sally. "We can sing
the songs at the party."

"When will we plan the lunch?"
asked Don. "We always need lunch
at a party."

"I will make cookies for the party,"
said Miss Day. "I can cut the cookies
so they will look like animals. We can
have milk with the cookies."

"Oh, that will be a fine lunch,"
said Billy. "I can hardly wait
to see the animal cookies."

The children were very busy all day
making things for their party.

First they began to draw pictures
of the way they would dress. They cut
paper to make their animal clothes.
Some of them used paint to make eyes
or a funny nose or mouth.

Don found a paper bag and cut holes in it. The holes were for eyes so he could see through the bag.

Miss Day helped Don make some ears on the paper bag. Then Don got paint and made a nose and a mouth.

"I have to make a long tail, too," said Don. "Then I can climb all over. Shall we leave our things here or take them home?"

"You had better leave them in school," answered Miss Day. "Have a rest or you will not be ready for a good time at the party."

The Party

The day of the animal party came. All through the morning the children were busy with their lessons.

"We will have one more lesson," said Miss Day. "After we read, we can put our books away. I know you want to get ready for the party."

Some children painted nice pictures to put up in the room. While they were making pictures, the other children went on with their plans.

Betty helped Jane draw something for a game. They put five holes in it. Sally and Mary began to plan what songs the children should be ready to sing at the party.

The boys asked if they should pick up papers or put things away.

"Do both," said Miss Day. "We must have a nice clean room for our party."

Some of the boys put up pictures that they had painted.

"I made some pictures of squirrels for the windows," said Billy. "Even the children on the playground can see these animals. I am going to ask Jack to climb up here and help put them on the windows."

Soon both boys were busy making the windows look pretty.

After lunch everyone began to dress
in animal clothes. What funny animals
they were.

Sally and Ann dressed the same way.
They had long pink ears. Each one
had a paper puff for a tail. They had
carrots to eat.

Betty looked like the little red hen.
She ran all around the room making
a clucking noise. Betty had to run
away from a big rooster that made its
wings flap and flap. It was only Jack.

"Now it is time for our game," said Sally. "You each need a bag. There are five holes. Try to throw your bag into one of those holes.

"If you try hard, you can put a bag into the hole with the 5 on it."

Everyone took turns throwing bags into the holes. Each one tried to hit the hole with a 5 on it.

Then Tom told them it was time for another game.

"In this game you will let us guess what animal you tell about. Jane may be the first one to let us guess."

Jane stood in front of the room.

"I am little and I am brown," said Jane. "I have two tiny feet. You have heard me cluck. Who am I?"

"You are Sandy," said Sally.

"Sally guessed it, so she has the next turn," said Tom.

"I am tiny," said Sally. "I have pink eyes. My nest is in a cage."

"You are one of the white mice," said Don.

Then Don stood up to have his turn.

"I have a long tail," said Don. "I like to climb all over. You have seen me at a circus. My front feet look like hands."

"You are a monkey," said Jack.

"Miss Day, may we sing our songs about pets?" asked Jane.

"Yes, you may have your music, now," answered Miss Day.

"We know a song about three mice," said Mary. "Let us sing that song."

After they were through singing, Miss Day asked the girls to help her. She gave them some pretty paper to put on the table. At one end of the table some children put bottles of milk. Then Miss Day brought in a big pan. Yellow paper was around the outside. She put the pan on the table.

The children looked inside the pan. They saw the cookies. Every cookie was cut to look like an animal.

Betty found a brown hen that looked like Sandy. Jack wanted a pony or a dog like Barky. Mary found white mice that had pink eyes.

"Here is a cookie rabbit," said Sally. "It looks like Twitchy Nose."

"I found little rabbits," said Ann. "They are like Puff's babies. Now we have a rabbit family again."

"We had animal pets and some clay animals and animal cookies," said Billy. "The animal cookies were the best of all."

"I think so, too, but we had fun with all of them," said Tom.

Read a Story

Frisky Finds a Home

Once there was a dog who needed
a home. The woman who owned Frisky
wanted to sell him.

Another woman came to buy Frisky.
This woman took Frisky home to play
with her baby. She thought Frisky
and the baby would have good times
together.

But—Frisky ran to the baby and
licked her face. He made her cry.
At night Frisky began to cry.
The noise made the baby cry again.

So—because Frisky woke her baby, the woman gave him to another woman who lived near her.

This woman had a fine little house for Frisky. It was near a flower bed.

But—Frisky dug holes in the flower beds. He pulled up some flowers.

"Oh, Frisky, see what you have done to my flower beds," said the woman. "I cannot keep you here. I never would have any flower garden."

So—she gave Frisky to a woman who came to do the family washing. This woman took Frisky home to play with her children.

But—he pulled down clean clothes the woman had washed. So the woman gave Frisky to two boys.

But—at lunch Frisky did not wait
for his turn to eat. He licked the
top of a cake. Early one morning
he climbed up on a nice clean bed.
He walked all over the top of it.
He woke the boys long before they
wanted to get up.

So—the boys gave Frisky to a man
who came to sell eggs at their house.

But—when Frisky got to the farm,
he made the poor ducks run so hard
they could not quack another quack.
He made the poor hens run so hard
they could not run any more. He ran
after the pigs, but the man made him
stop.

So—when a little girl named Susan
came along, the man was ready to give
Frisky away.

"If you do not want that little dog,
I should like to have him," said Susan.

"You may have him," said the man.

So—Susan took Frisky to her home.
Frisky was very happy there.

Susan knew that Frisky was only
a baby dog. If he woke her too early,
she did not care. She did not care
when he jumped on top of her bed.
If he broke her toys, she did not cry.
She let Frisky do anything he wanted
to do.

Susan knew that Frisky did not want
to do anything bad. He only wanted
to have fun.

209

The Fox and His Bag

One day a fox dug behind a tree.
He found a bumble-bee. So he put
the bumble-bee in his bag and off
he went.

By and by the fox came to a house.
He knocked at the door. A jolly woman
came to the door. The fox asked her
if he could leave his bag there
for a short time.

"Leave it on top of that table,"
answered the jolly woman.

"Do not look inside this bag,"
said the fox, and off he went.

The fox was hardly out of the house
when the jolly woman began to think
about the bag.

"What can be in that old bag?" she
said. "I will look inside and find out
if there is anything nice in it."

The woman opened the bag a tiny bit
at the top. Out flew the bumble-bee.
A rooster ate it.

In a short time, the fox came back.
He looked inside the bag. Then the fox
stamped his feet.

"Where is my bumble-bee?" he asked.

"I opened the bag just a tiny bit,"
said the woman. "A bumble-bee flew
out and my rooster ate it."

"You did not remember what I told
you," said the fox. "Now I must have
your rooster."

So he put the rooster into the bag.
He threw the bag over his back and
away he went.

The Rooster and the Pig

The fox went on to another house.
He went up the steps and knocked
at the door. A woman opened it.
The fox asked if he could leave
his bag there.

"You may leave it if you wish,"
answered the woman.

"Remember not to open the bag,"
the fox told her. He threw down
the bag and away he went.

The fox had hardly gone away
when the woman began to wonder
what was in the bag. She opened
the bag and out flew the rooster.

He flew over the mountain, and
that was the end of the rooster.

Soon the fox came back. He looked inside the bag. The rooster was gone.

"Where is my rooster?" he asked.

"Well, I began to wonder what was in the bag," said the woman. "I opened it and your rooster flew out."

"You did not remember what I told you," said the fox. "I must take your pig."

The fox put the pig into his bag. He tossed the bag on his back and off he went.

The Ox and the Boy

The fox went to another house and knocked. A woman opened the door.

"I want to leave this bag here," said the fox. "You must not open it. There is not anything in it for you."

"You may leave your bag here," said the woman.

When the fox was gone, the woman wondered what was in the bag. She opened it a bit and out came the pig.

An ox stood near. The ox caught the poor pig and tossed it up in the air. When it came down, that was the end of the pig.

When the fox came back to get his
bag, he saw that his pig was gone.

"My ox tossed your pig in the air,"
said the woman. "That was the end
of the pig."

"A woman should always remember
what she has been told. I must take
your ox," said the fox.

He took hold of the ox and tossed
it into his bag. He threw the bag
over his back and away he went.

The fox went on to another house
and knocked at the door. He asked
the woman if he could leave his bag.
He told her she must not open it.
He threw down the bag and went away.

Just as soon as the fox was gone,
the woman took hold of the big bag.
She began to wonder if there was
anything nice in the bag.

"I will fool that fox," she said.
"I will open the bag a tiny bit and
look inside."

She opened it and out walked the ox.

The woman's little boy saw the ox.
He got a stick. He made the ox run
over the hill and far away.

Just as soon as the fox came back,
he knew that the ox was gone.

"Where is my ox?" he asked.

"Oh, I opened the bag a tiny bit,"
answered the woman. "Your poor ox
walked out. My boy made the ox run
over the hill."

"You did not remember what I told
you," said the fox. "If my ox has gone
over the hill, I will take your boy."

He put the poor boy into his bag.
Then he threw the bag over his back
and away he went.

The Fox is Fooled

Just behind a hill, the fox saw a house. He knocked at the door and asked the woman if he could leave his bag.

"Yes, if you wish," she answered.

"There is not anything for you in it," said the fox. "Don't open the bag."

Then the fox went away again.

This woman was making some cookies. Um-um, how good the cookies smelled.

The woman's children said, "Please give us some of those fresh cookies."

When the boy in the bag smelled
the cookies, he called out.

"Please give me a cookie," he said.

The woman let the boy out of the bag.
She gave cookies to all the children.

"I will fool that fox," she said.
"I will put a big dog in his bag."

So she put a dog into the bag.

"That will fool him," she said.

The fox came back before long and
looked at his bag. He thought the bag
had not been opened. He tossed it
on his back and went over the hill.

After he had walked a long time,
the fox sat down to rest in a field
of sweet clover. He went to sleep.

It was almost night when the fox
woke up. He thought he would talk
to the boy. The fox opened the bag.

Out jumped the dog and it jumped
right on top of the fox.

That was the end of the fox.

Five Little Red Caps

Once upon a time there lived a man who was very poor. He was so poor he hardly had enough to eat. All his clothes were in rags.

The poor man had very little money. One day he looked at his money and wondered how he could get more.

At first the poor man could not think of anything to do. He watched some children playing in the park and thought of a way to get money.

"I will buy some little red caps," he said. "I can sell the red caps to the children."

The poor man had only enough money
to buy five little caps.

"This will be enough to start on,"
he said. "With all the money I get
from these caps, I can buy many more.
Everyone will want to wear red caps."

The man put the five caps into a bag.
He thought about the money he would
have soon.

"It will be fine to get enough money
to buy myself new clothes," he said.
"Then I will throw away these rags
that I have to wear now."

The man went all over his own
country and tried to sell the caps.
He could not get people to buy them.
No one wanted to wear red caps.

The man needed money to get
new clothes in place of his rags.
So he went to a country far away.

This country was warm. The man
walked up hill and walked down hill.
The poor man did not sell any caps.
At last he was very tired.

"I am warm and tired," he said.
"I will sit under this tree and
rest myself."

Soon the tired man was asleep.

The Monkeys See the Caps

Some monkeys were in that same tree. They had been watching the man.

The monkeys looked down at the bag. They wondered what was in it.

The little monkeys climbed down hand over hand, as only monkeys can do.

As soon as they were on the ground, they looked into the bag. When they saw the caps, they were very pleased.

Each monkey put his queer hands into the bag. Each one took hold of a red cap. The monkeys turned the caps round and round.

All the monkeys began to chatter
to each other. Maybe they chattered
about how pretty the red caps looked.
Maybe they chattered about making
the caps go round and round very fast.

One little monkey looked at the man.
He saw the old cap on the man's head.
Maybe he liked the way it looked.

The monkey put a cap on his head.
That pleased all the other monkeys.
They wanted to wear caps, too.

The monkeys put on the red caps
and went up into the tree.

After a while the man woke up.
He sat up and looked around.

"I was tired when I came here,"
he said. "I feel rested at last.
I will go on now. Maybe I can sell
the little red caps."

He picked up his bag and started out.

"My bag feels light," said the man.
"Maybe that is because I am not
so tired now."

As the man walked on, he began
to wonder why his bag seemed to be
light. At last he stopped and opened it.

"My red caps are gone!" he said.
"Oh, what shall I do!"

There was no hole in the bag, so
the caps did not fall out. The man
did not know what had happened.

The man looked along the road where
he had been walking. He did not see
any of the red caps.

He went back to the place where
he had gone to sleep. He looked, but
he did not see the caps.

At last he heard monkeys chattering
high in a tree. When he looked up,
he was surprised to see five monkeys.
Each one was wearing a red cap.

"So you are the ones who got
my little red caps," said the man.
"So that is what happened to them."

The man thought of a plan. He knew
that monkeys like to do what they see
people do. He thought he knew a way
to make them give him the red caps.

He took off his cap of rags and
turned it round and round.

The monkeys did the same thing.

The man threw his cap up high
in the air. Each time it came down
he caught it in both hands.

The monkeys threw their red caps
high in the air, too. When the caps
came down, the monkeys caught them.

"If my plan works, I will get
the caps with this next trick,"
said the man.

Then the man threw his old cap
high in the air again. He let it
fall to the ground. The monkeys
threw their caps high in the air.

As the caps came down, the man
picked them up. Soon the last one
was in his bag. Then away he went.

The monkeys did not want the man
to go away. They wanted those caps.
The monkeys chattered and chattered,
but they never did get the caps back.

Even to this day, all the monkeys
in that country like little red caps.
They have learned something, too.
If they want to keep their caps,
they must never toss them high
in the air.

Copy-Kitten

Copy-Kitten was a pretty kitty,
but no one would know it. That
was because Copy-Kitten always
tried to look like other animals.

Some days he tried to copy farm
animals. One day he would try
to copy the way some little pigs
dug into the ground. He found out
that he did not have the right kind
of a nose to be a pig.

When Copy-Kitten saw the chickens, he tried to copy them. He saw them flap their wings, but he had no wings to flap.

He heard the hens say cluck, cluck. He tried to say cluck, but he could only say mew, mew.

One day a circus came to the town. Copy-Kitten ran away from home to go to the circus grounds. He went to the animal tent.

First Copy-Kitten went to a cage.
There was a lion in the cage.

"That lion is just like a large cat,"
said Copy-Kitten. "I can copy that
lion."

The lion did not say anything.
He just walked across his cage.

Copy-Kitten walked up and down
in front of the cage.

"It is easy to copy the lion,"
he said. "I should have come
to the circus before. It is easy
to copy these animals."

Next Copy-Kitten saw a monkey
climb up on the side of his cage.

Copy-Kitten knew he could climb,
so he did not try to copy that.

Then Copy-Kitten saw the monkey
swing himself by his tail.

"I have a tail," said Copy-Kitten.
"It will be easy to swing that way."

Copy-Kitten tried to swing himself
by his tail. He learned that it was
not easy to do. He could not swing
like a monkey at all.

Copy-Kitten saw a big elephant.
He wanted to copy the elephant, but
he did not have a trunk.

The next animal Copy-Kitten saw
was a giraffe.

"What a long neck the giraffe has,"
said Copy-Kitten. "It will be easy
to make my neck as long as that."

Copy-Kitten put his head up as far
as he could. He could not make himself
look like a giraffe that way.

Then he took hold of his head and
pushed. He thought he could push
hard enough to make his neck long.

At last Copy-Kitten stopped trying
to make himself look like a giraffe.

"I thought it would be easy to copy these animals," said Copy-Kitten.

"It was easy to walk like a lion, but I could not swing like the monkey. I could not make myself have a long neck like a giraffe has."

So Copy-Kitten went home. He never did say anything about trying to copy the circus animals.

From that time, he did not even try to copy his mother. He was happy just to be himself.

The Ant and the Bird

A little black ant was walking near
the water. She went too near it.
Into the water went the ant and she
was almost drowned.

Just then a big bird was flying over
the water. The big bird saw the ant.
He did not want the ant to drown.
The bird thought of a way to keep
the ant from drowning.

The bird flew to the ground and picked up a blade of grass. He flew over the water. He let the blade of grass fall near the ant.

The ant got up on the blade of grass. Now she would not drown.

The blade of grass began to move along on the water. When the blade of grass had moved far enough along, the little ant was able to get out of the water.

About that time a country boy came
along. He had a small gun. He saw
the big bird flying over him.

The boy thought what a fine dinner
the big bird would be for him.

"Um-um," he said. "That big bird
will be a fine dinner for me."

Then the boy got his gun ready.
He was just ready to put up his gun,
when something happened.

The little ant saw that something awful might happen to the bird.

"The bird kept me from drowning," thought the ant. "Now I am going to do something for the bird."

The ant went over to the boy and bit his foot.

"Oh, oh, oh!" shouted the boy as he moved his foot. "My foot, my foot! Oh, oh!"

He turned to look at his foot. As he turned, the bird flew away.

When the boy looked up again, he saw the bird flying far, far away. The boy put down his gun.

"Well, there goes my fine dinner," he said. "I will not be able to get a bird that is so far away."

Then the boy looked for the ant.

"That ant bit me," he said. "It made me move so I could not use my gun. Where is that ant?"

But the little ant had moved away where the boy could not see her. She was under a blade of grass.

Something to Remember

In a country far away, there lived a giraffe and a lion. These animals liked each other, but they thought they were better than other animals.

One day the giraffe and the lion met at the foot of a hill. They talked of things they had seen.

"I went over the mountain one day," said the giraffe. "A woman has a farm there. Her name is Susan.

"Susan has a big farm, but you should see her coat! It is not so fine as ours. She wears a coat made of rags."

Then the lion asked if the giraffe
had seen any animals at the farm.

"Only an ox," answered the giraffe.
"Susan makes him work hard. He
was so tired he could hardly move."

"Did he work while you were there?"
asked the lion.

"No," said the giraffe. "Old Susan
went away. As soon as she was gone,
the ox fooled her. He stopped working
and got some hay for himself.

"He tossed some to me, but I threw it
back. I never eat anything like that."

"I wonder why that ox eats hay?"
said the giraffe. "I like to eat only
fresh green leaves. It is very easy
for me to get leaves. The poor ox
does not have a long neck. He cannot
get leaves to eat."

As he said this, the giraffe put up
his long neck and looked around.

"You look very fine," said the lion.

Then he waved his tail to show
that he thought himself fine, too.

Just then the giraffe heard monkeys
at the top of a tree.

"Just hear those monkeys!" he said.
"They never say anything. They only
chatter, chatter, chatter."

"The monkeys are very frisky, too,"
said the lion. "Some day they will
swing too hard and they will fall.
They are not one bit good and I
wish they would go away."

A bumble-bee came to the hill.
It flew from flower to flower and
then it flew high in the air.

"Bzzz, bzzz," said the bumble-bee,
as it flew round and round.

"What a queer head you have,"
said the lion as he shook his own
bushy head.

"Look at his funny short neck,"
said the giraffe. "Just what good
is an animal like you?"

"Maybe you will find out some day,"
said the bee, and he flew away.

The lion and the giraffe went
into the water to get a drink.
When they were ready to go home,
they could not get out.

"We may drown," said the lion.

"I tried to get out, but my feet
just stick here," said the giraffe.

The monkeys saw the two animals
in the water. One monkey went and
told the bumble-bee. The bumble-bee
flew over the mountain. He knocked
at the barn and woke the ox. As soon
as the ox heard about the lion and
the giraffe, he came to the water.

"Put out your long neck," he said
to the giraffe. "Get hold of my tail.
The lion can take hold of your tail.
I will pull you out."

At last the two animals were out
of the water. They thanked the ox.

"Thank the monkey," said the ox.
"Thank the bumble-bee. He knocked
at the barn door and woke me. I came
because I knew all animals should help
each other."

"You are right," said the giraffe.
"Many animals do things well, even
if they do not copy us."

"We must remember that some
animals can do even better than we
can," said the lion.

ACKNOWLEDGEMENTS

Grateful acknowledgement is made for permission to adapt and use copyrighted materials as follows:

"Little Yellow Chick" from *Little Yellow Chick*, by Letitia Scott from *Jack and Jill* magazine.

"Frisky Finds a Home" from *Frisky Finding a Home* by Dorothy and Marguerite Bryan. Copyright, 1938, by A. Marguerite Bryan. Reprinted by permission of Dodd, Mead & Company.

"The Fox and His Bag" from *Chimney Corner Stories*, edited by V. S. Hutchinson, courtesy of G. P. Putnam's Sons.

"The Five Little Red Caps" from *Folk Tales Retold* by Arnold and Beem. Courtesy of The Bruce Publishing Company.

"Copy-Kitten" from *Copy-Kitten*, by Helen and Alf Evers, copyright 1937, by Rand McNally & Company, Publishers.

"The Ant and the Bird" from *The Ant and the Dove* in *The Fables of La Fontaine* as translated by Margaret Wise Brown.

Acknowledgement is also made to the illustrators of *Down Our Way* as follows:

Fiore Mastri, contents page; pages 11-13, 16-25, 27-32, 35, 37-40, 42-51, 62-77, 80-86.

Gertrude Spaller Kinder, pages 87-126.

John Osebold, title page; pages 127-204.

Jean Busby, pages 1-10, 14-15, 26, 33, 34, 36, 41, 52-61, 78-79, 205-246.

TO THE TEACHER

Down Our Way is the basic second reader of The Developmental Reading Series. It is to be read after completion of *Happy Times*.

Down Our Way presents 295 new words at the rate of not more than 2 new words per page. All variants of these words are counted as new except those with endings 's, s, es, ed, ing.

There is a review of 342 words of the previous books of the series. The average repetition of all words is 30. The average repetition of new words is 14. The running words total 19,082.

WORD LIST

Unit I

1. . . . . . .
2. money
   Jack
3. July
   fourth
4. straw-
      berries
   picked
5. full
   much
6. cents
   our
7. garden
   almost
8. face
   brother
9. sister
   most
10. weeds
    please
11. early
    country
12. parade
    large

13. hurrah
14. done
    shouted
15. balloon
    monkeys
16. hands
    waved
17. right
    ate
18. feed
19. called
20. people
    begin
21. . . . . . .
22. best
23. bang
24. three
    clapped
25. lake
    week
26. row
    toys

27. sign
28. tourists
    camp
29. trailer
    swim
30. . . . . . .
31. Jim
72. first
    well
33. any
    bite
34. story
35. . . . . . .
36. . . . . . .
37. . . . . . .
38. . . . . . .
39. . . . . . .
40. . . . . . .
41. . . . . . .
42. . . . . . .

Unit II

43. town
44. vegetables
    sell
45. Mrs.
    buy
46. shall
    football
47. own
    thought
48. dinner
    fresh
49. use
50. myself
    keep
51. might
52. enough
    been
53. market
    fruit
54. peaches
    weigh

249

55. yellow

56. carry

57. dear
Peachy

58. cat
f-ff-t

59. milk

60. cannot
tell

61. bark
don't

62. dish
food

63. knew
side

64. bed

65. . . . . . .

66. dairy
Tim

67. trucks

68. bottles
machine

69. hear

70. next
wait

71. fire

72. . . . . . .

73. barn

74. better
than

75. . . . . . .

76. . . . . . .

77. firemen

78. . . . . . .

79. . . . . . .

80. . . . . . .

81. . . . . . .

82. . . . . . .

83. . . . . . .

84. . . . . . .

85. . . . . . .

86. . . . . . .

Unit III

87. chick

88. cross
waddling

89. because
puddle

90. flap

91. why
Warbling
Wren

92. fly
awful

93. Bouncing
Bunny
across

94. legs
bug

95. hard

96. invited
told

97. fine
along

98. does
clothes

99. strong
without

100. rest
should

101. way
took

102. only
talk

103. try

104. sit
bad

105. these
warm

106. off

107. . . . . . .

108. . . . . . .

109. . . . . . .

110. sheep
pig

111. build
goose

112. stuffed
together

113. met

114. hen
rooster

115. dug

116. . . . . . .

117. . . . . . .

118. . . . . . .

119. . . . . . .

120. . . . . . .

121. . . . . . .

122. . . . . . .

123. . . . . . .

124. . . . . . .

125. . . . . . .

126. . . . . . .

Unit IV

127. Mary

128. calf
asleep

129. cow
present

130. licking
washes

131. hardly
wobbly

132. father
breakfast

133. while
plenty

134. nice
pen

250

135. seven
short

136. Tiny
kind

137. learn
care

138. grows
Spot

139. kept
still

140. goes

141. pail
drink

142. hold
nose

143. once
bottom

144. caught

145. greedy
floor

146. happened
upon

147. such

148. different
able

149. bring
even

150. ......

151. ice

152. geese

153. frog
green

154. s-s-s-s

155. Siz

156. started
stay

157. ......

158. ......

159. ......

160. ......

161. ......

162. ......

163. ......

164. ......

165. ......

166. ......

Unit V

167. books

168. lessons
Miss

169. read
Don

170. family
Sally

171. brought
carrots

172. clean

173. twitchy
puff

174. everyone
babies

175. stood
through

176. Sandy
same

177. mice
cage

178. eyes

179. found
room

180. picture
seem

181. paper
busy

182. pan
inside

183. front
pink

184. both
climb

185. cluck
making

186. ......

187. outside
men

188. play-
ground
clay

189. need
bag

190. table
end

191. cut
paint

192. ......

193. plans
dress

194. draw

195. song
cookies

196. or

197. holes

198. ......

199. ......

200. ......

201. ......

202. ......

203. ......

204. ......

Unit VI

205. ......

206. Frisky
woman

207. woke
flower

251

208. top
poor

209. Susan
anything

210. bumble-
bee
knocked

211. bit

212. remember
threw

213. gone
wonder

214. tossed

215. ox
air

216. ......

217. fool
hill

218. ......

219. ......

220. ......

221. ......

222. caps
rags

223. wear

224. last
tired

225. round

226. chatter
maybe

227. ......

228. high

229. ......

230. ......

231. Copy-
Kitten
copy

232. say

233. lion
easy

234. swing
himself

235. giraffe
neck

236. ......

237. ant
drowned

238. blade
move

239. gun

240. foot

241. ......

242. ......

243. ......

244. ......

245. ......

246. ......

247. ......